The First Christmas Tree

and other Christmas Stories

KT-434-073

Miles Kelly

First published in 2015 by Miles Kelly Publishing Ltd
Harding's Barn, Bardfield End Green, Thaxted, Essex, CM6 3PX, UK

Copyright © Miles Kelly Publishing Ltd 2015

2 4 6 8 10 9 7 5 3

Publishing Director Belinda Gallagher
Creative Director Jo Cowan
Editorial Director Rosie Neave
Senior Editor Sarah Parkin
Design Manager Joe Jones
Production Elizabeth Collins, Caroline Kelly
Reprographics Stephan Davis, Jennifer Cozens, Thom Allaway
Assets Lorraine King

All rights reserved. No part of this publication may be reproduced, stored in a
retrieval system, or transmitted by any means, electronic, mechanical, photocopying,
recording or otherwise, without the prior permission of the copyright holder.

ISBN 978-1-78209-824-9

Printed in China

British Library Cataloguing-in-Publication Data
A catalogue record for this book is available from the British Library

ACKNOWLEDGEMENTS
The publishers would like to thank the following artists who have contributed to this book:

Front cover: Simona Sanfilippo (Plum Pudding Illustration Agency)

Inside illustrations:
Decorative frame Rachel Cloyne (Pickled Ink)
Jesus is Born in Bethlehem Tamsin Hinrichsen (Advocate Art)
The First Christmas Tree Natalia Moore (Advocate Art)
The Elves and the Shoemaker Simona Sanfilippo (Plum Pudding Illustration Agency)
Christmas Every Day Florencia Denis (Plum Pudding Illustration Agency)

Made with paper from a sustainable forest

www.mileskelly.net
info@mileskelly.net

Contents

Jesus is Born in Bethlehem

Anon

Christmas is traditionally the time when Christians celebrate the birth of Jesus, who they believe is the son of God. This is the story of what happened when Jesus was born.

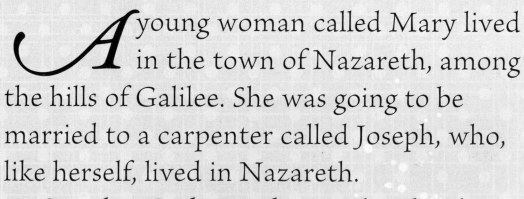

A young woman called Mary lived in the town of Nazareth, among the hills of Galilee. She was going to be married to a carpenter called Joseph, who, like herself, lived in Nazareth.

One day God sent the angel Gabriel to

Mary with a message. Mary, when she saw and heard the angel, was a little frightened but the angel told her he had some good news for her. The Son of God was coming into the world very soon, and he would be born as Mary's little child. Gabriel said that when the baby was born, Mary should call him Jesus.

About this time Caesar Augustus, the great Emperor of Rome, sent word to Herod, his ruler in Palestine, that he was to take a census of the Jews. Everybody's name had to be written down, as well as their age and many other things about them. Every twenty years Augustus had a census taken, so that he might know how much money the Jews ought to pay him in taxes, and how many soldiers he could demand they send him.

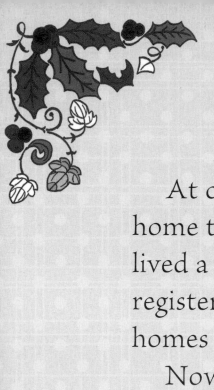

At census time, people had to go to their home towns where their fathers' fathers lived a long time ago, and had to register there instead of in the homes where they lived now.

Now, both Joseph and Mary belonged to the family of the great King David, who was born in Bethlehem. So Mary had to prepare for a long journey, and go with her husband to Bethlehem. She rode on a donkey and Joseph led it

carefully over the rough roads.

Bethlehem is on top of a hill, and people have to climb up a steep road to get into the town. When Joseph and Mary reached Bethlehem, Mary was very tired, and so Joseph went to look for an inn in which they could stay the night. An inn is a large house that people stay at when they are on a journey. There were many inns in Bethlehem, but Mary and Joseph, after their long journey from Nazareth, could not find one that had room.

In the end, one innkeeper said he had no rooms for them, but, if they wanted, they could sleep in the stable with the animals. And so, because there was no room for them in the inn, Mary and Joseph went into that stable to sleep, and in that stable Jesus was born.

Mary wrapped him in swaddling cloths, which were strips of cloth wound snugly round him to help him feel warm and safe, and she laid him in a manger, the place where the animals' food is put.

On the hill where Bethlehem stood, shepherds took their flocks to feed. There were

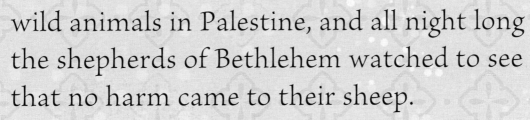

wild animals in Palestine, and all night long the shepherds of Bethlehem watched to see that no harm came to their sheep.

That night an angel of the Lord appeared to them and a bright light shone round about them. The shepherds were terrified, but the angel said, "Don't be afraid, I've come to tell you wonderful news. A king has been born this night in the city of David. You will find the baby wrapped in swaddling cloths and lying in a manger."

And then the sky was filled with a wonderful light, and angels singing, "Glory to God in the highest, and on Earth peace, good will towards men."

When the light faded, the song ended and the angels returned to heaven, the shepherds climbed quickly over the hillside to Bethlehem. And there, in the stable near

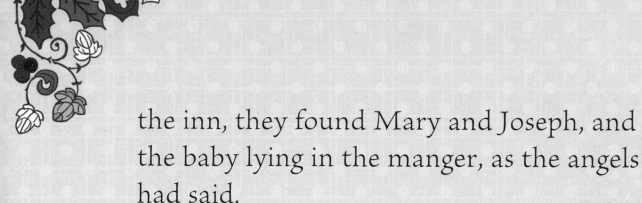

the inn, they found Mary and Joseph, and the baby lying in the manger, as the angels had said.

Jesus had some other visitors too. A long way on the eastern side of the River Jordan, there were countries where people used to watch the Sun and the Moon and the stars very carefully. If they saw anything new and strange in the heavens, they thought it meant that something wonderful was going to happen on Earth.

One day these wise men saw a bright star that they had never seen before. And as they looked at it they felt sure that its message was that a great King of the Jews had been born in Judaea, a person they called the Christ. So they took expensive gifts of gold and sweet-smelling stuff – such as people gave to kings in those days – and

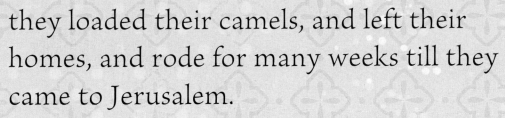

they loaded their camels, and left their homes, and rode for many weeks till they came to Jerusalem.

When they got there they said, "Where is he that is born King of the Jews? For we have seen his star in the East, and have come to worship him."

When Herod the ruler heard about these wise men he was troubled. He didn't want any kings coming along who might challenge him. He sent for the best priests, and other clever men, and asked them where Christ would be born.

They said to him, "In Bethlehem of Judaea." They had read this in the Bible.

Then Herod said to the wise men, "Go and search out the young child, and when you have found him, come back and tell me where he is, so that I may come and see him

also." But really Herod planned to kill Jesus.

The wise men agreed and then they went away to Bethlehem. The bright star led them on till it stopped above the place where the baby Jesus was.

When they came into the house (there was room in the inn now) they saw the baby with Mary, his mother. They knelt down before him, as if to a great king, and they gave him their gifts – gold, frankincense and myrrh. But the wise men did not go back to Herod. God told them in a dream not to go. So they went home another way instead.

But the danger of Herod finding out about Jesus was still there. So after the wise men were gone, God's angel came to Joseph in his sleep, and said to him, "Take the baby and his mother, and escape into Egypt, for Herod will seek the child to kill him."

So Joseph at once got up, and took Jesus and Mary and put them on his donkey. He led them quietly out of Bethlehem and away to Egypt, where they would be safe.

The First Christmas Tree

An extract from *The Life and Adventures of Santa Claus*
by L Frank Baum

*This is part of a story telling how Santa Claus
lives in a place called Laughing Valley, but goes out
into the world to bring joy to children.*

*C*laus had always kept his promise, returning to the Laughing Valley by daybreak, but only the swiftness of his reindeer has enabled him to do this, for he travels all over the world.

He loved his work and he loved the brisk

night ride on his sledge and the gay tinkle of the sleigh bells. On that first trip with the ten reindeer only Glossie and Flossie wore bells, but each year after for eight years Claus carried presents to the children of the Gnome King, and that good-natured monarch gave him in return a string of bells at each visit, so that finally every one of the ten deer was supplied. You may imagine what a merry tune the bells played as the sledge sped over the snow.

The children's stockings were so long that it required a great many toys to fill them, and soon Claus found there were other things besides toys that children love.

So he sent some of the fairies, who were always his good friends, into the Tropics. They returned with great bags full of oranges and bananas that they had plucked

from the trees. And other fairies flew to the wonderful Valley of Phunnyland, where delicious candies and bonbons grew thickly

on the bushes, and returned laden with many boxes of sweetmeats for the little ones. On each Christmas Eve, Santa Claus placed these things in the long stockings, together with his toys, and the children were glad to get them, you may be sure.

There are also warm countries where there is no snow in winter, but Claus visited them as well as the colder countries, for there were little wheels inside the runners of his sledge that permitted it to run as smoothly over bare ground as on the snow. And the children who lived in the warm countries learned to know the name of Santa Claus as well as those who lived nearer to the Laughing Valley.

Once, just as the reindeer were ready to start on their yearly trip, a fairy came to Claus and told him of three little children who lived beneath a rough tent of skins on a broad plain, where there were no trees. These poor children were miserable and unhappy, for their parents neglected them. Claus decided to visit these children before

he returned home, and during his ride he picked up the bushy top of a pine tree, which the wind had broken off, and placed it in his sledge.

It was nearly morning when the reindeer stopped before the lonely tent of skins where the poor children lay asleep. Claus planted the bit of pine tree in the sand and stuck many candles on the branches. Then he hung some of his prettiest toys on the tree, as well as several bags of candies.

The First Christmas Tree

It did not take long to do all this, for Santa Claus works quickly, and when all was ready he lit the candles and, thrusting his head in at the opening of the tent, he shouted, "Merry Christmas little ones!"

With that he leapt into his sledge and was out of sight before the children, rubbing the sleep from their eyes, could come out to see who had called them.

You can imagine the wonder and joy of those little ones, who had never in their lives known a real pleasure before, when they saw the tree, sparkling with lights that shone brilliant in the grey dawn and hung with toys enough to make them happy

for years to come.

They joined hands and danced around the tree, shouting and laughing, until they were obliged to pause for breath. And their parents also came out to look and wonder, and thereafter had more respect and consideration for their children, since Santa Claus had honoured them with such beautiful gifts.

The idea of the Christmas tree pleased Claus, and so the following year he carried many of them in his sledge and set them up in the homes of poor people who seldom saw trees, and placed candles and toys on the branches.

Of course he could not carry enough trees in one load for all who wanted them, but in some homes the fathers were able to get trees and have them all ready for Santa

Claus when he arrived. And these Claus always decorated as prettily as possible, and hung with toys enough for all the children who came to see the tree lit.

These ideas and the generous manner in which they were carried out made the children long for that one night in the year when their friend Santa Claus should visit them. As such anticipation is very pleasant and comforting, the little ones gleaned much happiness by wondering what would happen when Santa Claus next arrived.

for two pairs with the money.

He cut them out in the evening, and next day, with fresh courage, was about to go to work. But he had no need to, for when he got up, the shoes were finished, and two more people eagerly bought them. That gave him so much money that he was able to buy leather for four pairs of shoes.

Early next morning he found the four pairs finished, and so it went on – what he cut out in the evening was finished in the morning. In a couple of weeks the shoemaker was living very comfortably, with plenty of money for food, and he even had enough to buy himself and his wife fine new clothes.

Now, it happened on the day before Christmas Eve, when he had cut out shoes, that he said to his wife, "How would it be

24

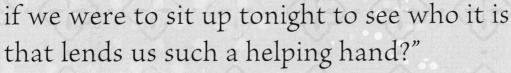

if we were to sit up tonight to see who it is that lends us such a helping hand?"

His wife agreed, lit a candle, and then they both hid themselves in the corner of the room behind the clothes that were hanging there.

At midnight there came two little raggedy men, who sat down at the shoemaker's table, took up the cut-out work, and began with their tiny fingers to stitch, sew and hammer so neatly and quickly, that the shoemaker could not believe his eyes. They did not stop till everything was finished and stood complete on the table, then they ran swiftly away.

The next day his wife said, "The little men have made us rich, and we ought to show them how grateful we are. Let us give them a Christmas present, for tomorrow

is Christmas Day. I will make them little shirts, coats, waistcoats and trousers, and will even knit them strong socks, and you shall make them each a pair of shoes."

The shoemaker agreed, and in the evening, when they had everything ready, they laid out the presents on the table with wine and cake, and hid themselves to see how the little men would behave.

At midnight they came skipping in, and were about to set to work, but, instead of the leather ready cut out, they found the charming little clothes.

At first they were surprised, then extremely delighted. With the greatest speed they put on and smoothed down the pretty clothes, singing,

"Now we're dressed so fine and neat,
Why cobble more for others' feet?"

Then they drank the wine and ate the cake, and hopped and danced about, and leapt over chairs and tables, and then out at the door.

The next day was Christmas Day, and they did not appear, nor any day after that, but the shoemaker did well as long as he lived and had good luck in everything he did. And every Christmas Eve after that, he and his wife poured a glass of wine and drank a toast to their secret helpers.

Christmas Every Day

By William Dean Howells

*O*nce there was a little girl who liked Christmas so much that she wanted it to be Christmas every day of the year. And as soon as Thanksgiving was over, she began to send postcards to the old Christmas Fairy to ask if she might have her wish. But the old Fairy never answered. So

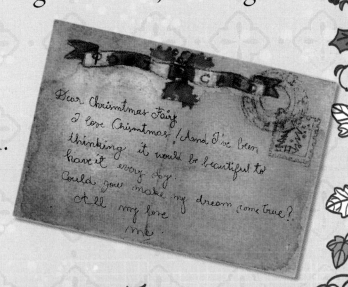

Dear Christmas Fairy,
I love Christmas! And I've been thinking it would be beautiful to have it every day.
Could you make my dream come true?
All my love
me.

29

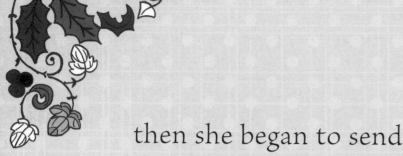

then she began to send her letters.

The day before Christmas she got a letter from the Fairy, saying she might have it Christmas every day for a year, and then they would see about having it longer. The little girl was a good deal excited already, preparing for the old-fashioned, once-a-year Christmas that was coming the next day, and perhaps the Fairy's promise didn't make such an impression on her as it would have made at some other time.

She went to bed early, so as to let Santa Claus have a chance at the stockings. In the morning she was up the first of anybody, and found hers all lumpy with packages of candy and oranges and rubber balls, and all kinds of small presents. Then she waited around till the rest of the family were up, and she was the first to burst into the

library, when the doors were opened, and look at the large presents laid out on the table – books, and boxes of stationery, and dolls, and little stoves, and skates, and snow shovels, and photograph frames, and boxes of watercolours, and nougat, and candied cherries, and dolls' houses – and the big Christmas tree, lighted and standing in a waste basket in the middle.

She had a splendid Christmas all day. She ate so much candy that she did not want any breakfast. Then she went round giving the presents she had got for other people, and came home and ate turkey and cranberry for dinner, and plum pudding and nuts and raisins and oranges and more candy. And then she went out and sledged, and came in with a stomach ache. They had a light supper, and pretty early everybody

went to bed cross.

The little girl slept very heavily, and she slept very late, but she was wakened at last by the other children dancing round her bed, with their stockings full of presents in their hands.

"What is it?" said the little girl, and she rubbed her eyes.

"Christmas! Christmas! Christmas!" they all shouted.

"Nonsense! It was Christmas yesterday."

Her brothers and sisters just laughed. "We don't know about that. It's Christmas today, anyway."

Then all at once it flashed on the little girl that the Fairy was keeping her promise, and her year of Christmases was beginning. She was dreadfully sleepy, but she sprang up like a lark – a lark that had overeaten and gone to bed cross – and darted into the library. There it was again! Books, and boxes of stationery, and the rest, and there was the Christmas tree blazing away, and the family picking out their presents, but looking pretty sleepy. Her father was

perfectly puzzled, and her mother ready to cry. Her father said it seemed to him they had something just like it the day before, but he supposed he must have dreamed it.

Well, the next day, it was just the same thing all over again, but everybody was getting crosser. The little girl began to get frightened, keeping the secret all to herself. She wanted to tell her mother, but she didn't dare to. And she was ashamed to ask the Fairy to take back her gift, it seemed ungrateful, but she hardly knew how she could stand it, for a whole year.

So it went on and on, and it was Christmas on St Valentine's Day and Washington's Birthday, just the same as any day, and it didn't skip even the First of April, though everything was a trick that day, and that was some little relief.

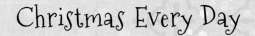

After a while, turkeys got to be about a thousand dollars apiece, and cranberries – well, they asked a diamond apiece for cranberries. All the woods and orchards were cut down for Christmas trees, and after a while they had to make Christmas trees out of rags. But there were plenty of rags, because people got so poor, buying presents, that they couldn't get any new clothes, and they just wore their old ones to tatters.

Well, after it had gone on for about three or four months, the little girl, whenever she came into the room in the morning and saw those great ugly, lumpy stockings dangling

at the fireplace, and the disgusting presents around everywhere, used to just sit down and burst out crying. In six months she was perfectly exhausted – she couldn't even cry anymore. About the beginning of October she was sitting down on dolls wherever she found them, and by Thanksgiving she was throwing her presents across the room.

By that time people didn't carry presents around nicely any more. They flung them over the fence or through the window. And, instead of taking great pains to write 'For dear Papa,' or 'Jimmie,' or 'Jennie,' or whoever it was, they used to write, 'Take it, you horrid old thing!' and then go and bang it against the front door.

Nearly everybody had built barns to hold their presents, but pretty soon the barns overflowed, and then they used to let them lie out in the rain, or anywhere. Sometimes the police used to come and tell people

to shovel their presents off the sidewalk, or they would arrest them.

Well, before Thanksgiving it had leaked out who had caused all these Christmases.

The little girl had suffered so much that she had talked about it in her sleep, and after that hardly anybody would play with her.

The very next day the little girl began to send letters to the Christmas Fairy to stop it. But it didn't do any good, so it went on till it came to the old, once-a-year Christmas Eve. The little girl fell asleep, and when she woke up in the morning she found that it wasn't Christmas at last, and wasn't ever going to be any more.

Well, there was the greatest rejoicing all over the country. The people met together everywhere, and kissed and cried for joy. The city carts went around and gathered up all the candy, and dumped it into the river. And the whole of the United States was one blaze of bonfires, where the children were burning up their gift books and presents of

all kinds. They had the greatest time!

The little girl went to thank the old Fairy because she had stopped it being Christmas, and she said she hoped the Fairy would see that Christmas never, never came again.

The Fairy frowned and asked her if she was sure. This made the little girl think, and she said she would be willing to have it Christmas about once in a thousand years, and then she said a hundred, and then she said ten, and at last she got down to one. The Fairy said that was the good old way that had pleased people ever since Christmas began, and she agreed to the little girl's request.

Then the little girl said, "What are your shoes made of?"

The Fairy said, "Leather."

And the little girl said, "Well then, bargain's done forever," and skipped off, and hippity-hopped the whole way home, because she was just so glad.